C701072518

10 **THINGS YOU**

cse 8/12

-6 OCT 2012

- 5 DEC 2012

D0589177

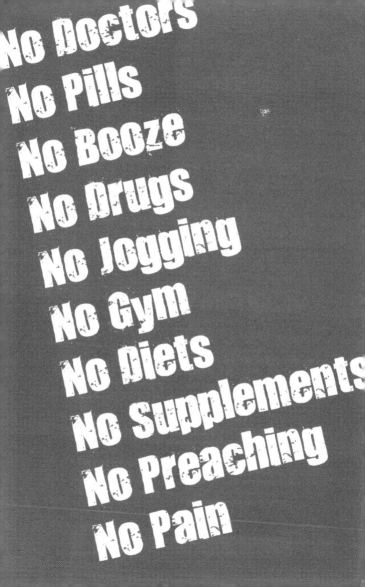

You can start feeling better about 10 minutes from now

Like loads of people, you're not feeling great at the moment.

Your system's a bit sluggish. You're miserable some of the time. You think your life could be better all round, but nothing seems to cheer you up these days.

So here's the good news: you can start to feel better in a few minutes from now. All you have to do is finish reading this book and then make some small, easy changes to what you do each day.

More good stuff

No broccoli
is involved

You *will* have to get off the couch and walk about a bit. You'll also have to say no to a burger or two, but you won't have to wear Lycra shorts and we promise not to turn you into a vegetarian.

The thing is this: there are things you can do and things you can eat that *make you feel happier straight away.*

Amazingly, some foods actually help you get going to face the day. Some activities give you a boost – direct to the brain.

When you combine the two – eating *and* doing certain things – those fed up feelings can disappear (along with spots and even excess weight sometimes).

And it's easy. You just make ten small changes to your daily routine.

Are you ready?

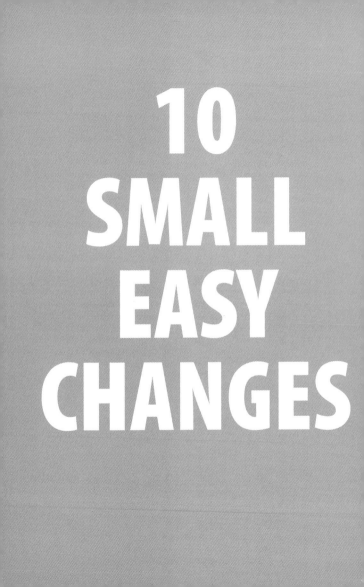

10 SMALL EASY CHANGES

This way to Small Easy Change No.1

Small Easy
Change 1

THE ESCALATOR BUSINESS

Turn your back on lifts and escalators

Exercise is good for you. So good that when you do it, your body says 'thanks' by sending happy chemicals to your brain.

But who's got the time or money to go to the gym?

Instead, use the stairs rather than the lift or escalator when you're out shopping, at work or at school.

Climbing stairs is one of the best ways there is to get fitter and get that happy stuff into your head. In fact climbing stairs each day for a year is the same as climbing a large mountain. Great view isn't it!

Decide to do it next time you're out. Then decide to keep on doing it and always take the stairs. Your brain will get happier and happier.

While you're climbing the stairs at the shopping centre here's what to buy...

Small Easy Change 2

THE BANANA THING

Monkeys aren't stupid

Did you ever see a depressed chimp?

Not many people know this, but bananas can help produce the same happy chemical in your head as a pill. What's more, they give you a steady supply of energy. And bananas are available off prescription.

Be honest, ways to feel better don't get much easier than this.

1. Eat a banana.

2. That's it. Eat the banana.

One a day is good, and here's a way to make those good feelings even stronger – walk to the shops and use the stairs when you go and buy your bananas.

Small Easy
Change No.3
next

PUT ON YOUR 'WOW' GLASSES

The world is amazing when you really look at it

When was the last time you went outside and really noticed what's there? The wind, the warmth, the cold, the trees, the flowers, the shops and the sky.

When you stop and think, the world is full of stuff that makes you go 'Wow!'

People who recover from really bad times often say they appreciate things they used to take for granted. So put on your special glasses and see the world for the amazing place it is.

Even better, do it with a friend. Go for walks together, talk about good times, and you'll soon get those happy chemicals coursing through your brain

YOU OLD SMOOTHIE

Are you fed up with hearing about 5 a day?

Even if you like fruit and vegetables, it's hard to have five portions a day.

Trouble is, you really do need that much fibre. Without it, your system clogs up and you get all sad and sluggish.

So here's a cheat – drink smoothies. They're just mashed up fruit and veg, usually with most of the good stuff left in, and just one glass a day does the trick.

Ready? Walk briskly to the shop, buy a carton of smoothie, walk briskly home, drink one glass of smoothie, feel smug.

DOING
PORRIDGE

Breakfast makes you happy

It's amazing but it's true. When you do without breakfast, your body doesn't get the right kind of start and it sulks all day, demanding coffee or snacks and often giving you a headache by lunchtime.

But when you eat a bowl of porridge or muesli each morning, you don't need all those snacks, your digestion works better and your mood improves no end.

Porridge and muesli work like – how can we put this – drain unblockers. After a few days they clear your system out and you feel better all round.

Walk quickly to the shops and buy some, now.

HEAVY
BREATHING

Faster, faster

You already exercise. If you do household chores, they're exercise. When you clean the car or do the garden, that's exercise. When you lift or move things at work or school, that's exercise.

So why don't you feel better? Because you're not doing it fast enough. Exercise only works properly (and produces happy chemicals) when you get out of breath and your heart starts pumping.

So do the housework faster. Clean the car quicker. Move those files or shift those boxes at a run (always being careful not to take risks or hurt yourself of course).

Oh, and while doing it...

You could try the next idea

MAKE
A NOTE
OF THIS

Don't suffer in silence

Music cheers you up. Obvious? So why are you sitting there in silence? Silence is just a space for you to think about your worries in.

Put some of your favourite music on. Do it now. Play music while you're exercising and getting out of breath and it'll send even more happy stuff to your brain.

Play music while you're walking briskly to the shops. Play music while you're sitting around.

But don't play sad stuff, or songs that remind you of unhappy times. Keep it upbeat and you'll get an instant lift.

TAKE
ONE
AWAY

This one saves money too

Eating too much fast food or takeaway food is a great way to get really down.

Did you see that experiment where a man ate nothing but fast food? He felt depressed and really unhealthy inside a couple of weeks.

So here's what you do: cut out one burger or takeaway a week. Just one. Replace it with something you make yourself (easy things like beans on toast are fine).

Within just a week or so, you'll start to feel lighter, fitter and happier. And a bit better off.

Small Easy Change 9

HELP!

It ain't what you do, it's who you do it for

Do a small kindness for someone else, every day, and you'll feel even better than they do. What's more, you'll feel good straight away.

It doesn't have to be a big thing like sometimes helping at a soup kitchen or drop-in centre (although those would be great, of course).

You can just as easily get a lift in your mood by helping someone with their work, writing a letter of thanks for being your friend, cooking a meal or spending time with a person who needs the company.

Go on, sit down now and plan one or two helpful things you're going to do for other people this week. They'll feel good, but you'll feel even better!

Final idea coming up next

THE HAPPY LIST

My Good Times

Remember the good things

When you're down it's easy to forget the good times – times you've succeeded in something, happy times with friends, things that make you smile and times you did something to help someone else.

So remember them. Each evening, sit down and write down three things that you:

have enjoyed

felt was a job well done

or helped you feel close to someone else

After a few days, you'll have a list of great things that you can look back on, and this will help you feel a lot better.

What you think about affects how you feel. Focus on the good things and you'll be happier for it!

Well?

WHAT ARE YOU WAITING FOR?

Go and get that banana

At the beginning of this book, we promised you could start feeling better in ten minutes. It's time, so here's what you do:

If it's daylight, go out, walk briskly to the corner shop and buy a couple of bananas. Walk quickly home and eat them.

If it's night and the shops are closed, walk up and down your stairs for ten minutes, or long enough to get your heart pumping.

Whichever you do, you'll send the happy stuff to your brain and your mood will start to lift.

Do these things regularly, along with the other small changes in this book and you'll be amazed how your mood (and your health) will improve!

Good Luck!

WHERE TO GET EVEN MORE HELP

(but no broccoli)

For more tips on feeling better, go to
www.llttf.com
It's all free, and it's packed with
ways to lift your mood and start
having a healthier life.
There are links on there, too, so you
can connect with other people who are
using food and exercise to feel great.
And don't worry, last time we looked, very
few vegetables were mentioned.

ABOUT THIS BOOK

With websites receiving over 4 million hits a month and a wealth of supporting research data, the Five Areas Approach on which this book is based, devised by Dr Chris Williams, is one of the most widely-used CBT systems in the world.

Cognitive Behavioural Therapy (CBT) has a strong evidence base for helping people with low mood, anxiety and a growing range of other common mental and physical health difficulties.

Want to learn more about you? Turn things around in your life for the better? The Five Areas Approach can help you to do this. It takes the proven CBT model and makes it accessible and practical so that you can have the tools you need to help change things in your life – fast.

Please visit the Five Areas websites – www.llttf.com (free life skills course), www.llttfshop.com (bookshop) and www.fiveareasonline.com (online books) – to discover more about this work and see the other resources on offer.

Dr Chris Williams is Professor of Psychosocial Psychiatry at the University of Glasgow, UK, and is a past-President of the British Association for Behavioural and Cognitive Psychotherapies (www.babcp.com) – the lead body for CBT in the UK, trustee of the charities Anxiety UK and Triumph over Phobia and is a well-known CBT workshop leader and researcher.

PICK ME UP

Turn your life around – fast!

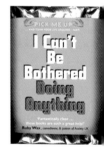